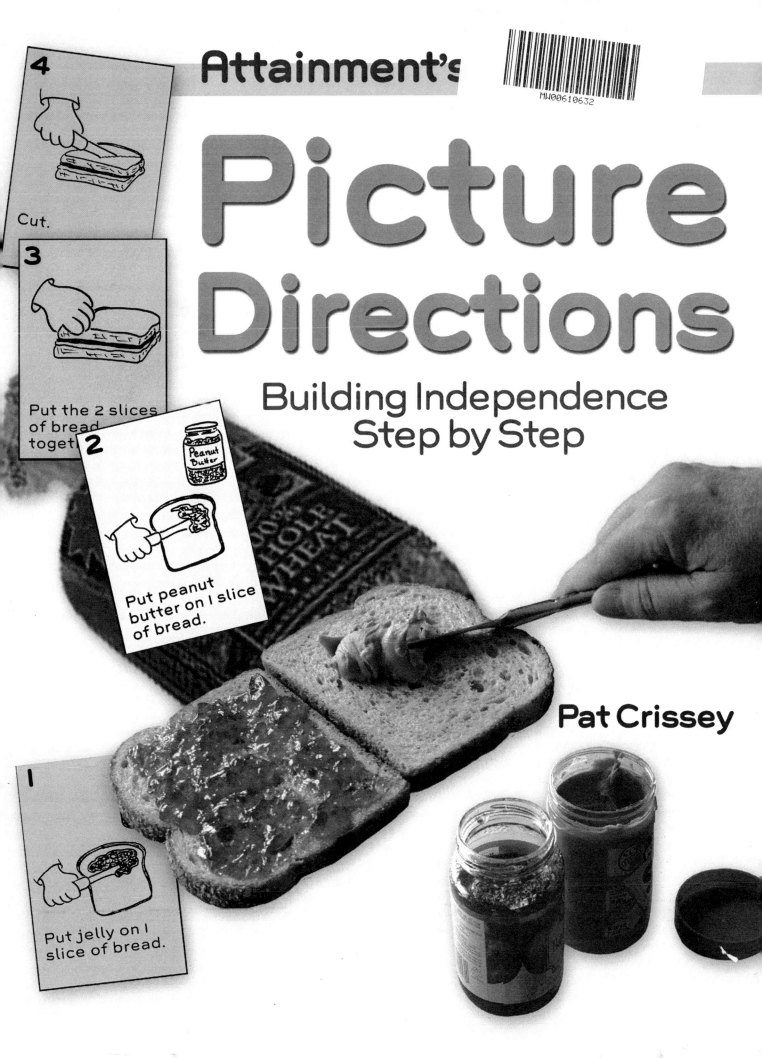

Attainment's

Picture
Directions

Building Independence
Step by Step

Pat Crissey

4 Cut.

3 Put the 2 slices of bread together.

2 Put peanut butter on I slice of bread.

I Put jelly on I slice of bread.

Win/Mac CD

This CD contains a printable PDF of the entire book. You can review and print pages from your computer. The PDF (portable document format) file requires Acrobat Reader software. If you have Acrobat Reader already on your computer, run the program and then open the file using PDGuide.pdf from the CD.

To Install Acrobat Reader for Windows:
Run ARINSTALL.EXE provided on the CD. After installation, run Acrobat Reader; then open using PDGuide.pdf

To install Acrobat Reader for Mac:
Run Reader Installer. After installation, open using PDGuide.pdf

Pat Crissey, Author and Illustrator
Tom Kinney, Editor
Jo Reynolds, Cover Art
Lynn Chrisman, Graphic Designer

An Attainment Company Publication
©2005 Attainment Company, Inc. All Rights Reserved.
Printed in the United States of America.

ISBN: 1-57861-553-4

Attainment Company, Inc.
P.O. Box 930160 • Verona, Wisconsin 53593-0160 USA
Phone: 1-800-327-4269 • Fax: 1-800-942-3865
www.AttainmentCompany.com

Picture Directions

Life Skills...................................98

Play Skills..................................120

Discovery....................................138

Appendix.....................................150

About the Author

Pat Crissey has worked in the field of special education for over twenty years, as a special education teacher and autism consultant. She received a Bachelor of Science degree in special and elementary education from Illinois State University and completed graduate work in special education from Western Oregon University. She lives in McMinnville, Oregon with her husband, has three grown children and one young granddaughter.

How to Use Picture Directions

The tasks presented in this book were carefully selected by a veteran teacher to avoid any safety issues (no sharp knives, no stoves or microwaves, no hot glue guns). While some of the tasks might get a little messy, none should be a complete disaster. These are tasks that most young children can do independently, with the use of picture directions and a little initial instruction. The picture directions pages are all reproducible so they can be photocopied and cut out, colored or used on communications boards again and again.

The first tasks presented in the book are ones that can be done repeatedly, even on a daily basis: Making some juice, making a sandwich, folding laundry. These are introduced first because in the beginning the children will learn how to use picture directions as well as how to perform the given tasks. Once a child is able to follow the sequence of picture directions, then other tasks can be introduced.

While all of the activities provided in this book are selected for the young or developmentally delayed student with beginning level skills and concepts, there still exists a range of skill levels within the different activities. A table, which ranks the different activities according to level of difficulty, is provided in the back of the book on page 150. It is designed to provide a quick reference to aid in selecting appropriate activities for a child, depending on his or her current level of functioning.

It is important to remember that the number one objective of using picture directions is to teach the child how to follow written directions independently. The second, and lesser, objective is to perform the actual tasks. Therefore, the child should never be rushed through to completion, but should be encouraged to try to figure out what to do.

The cleaning up process has not been included in the directions for a couple of reasons. One is to keep the directions short and easy to follow. The other is that cleaning up is not highly motivating for most kids. To become independent in using directions, the child needs to be motivated to complete the task. Cleaning up is probably going to take more adult supervision.

Providing prompts or picture cues for clean up is recommended, because this is an important life skill. With many of the activities, providing a plastic tub where everything can be put afterwards is all that is needed. Having a visual checklist for putting the cap back on the glue stick and putting lids on containers, etc., may be helpful.

►Getting Ready

Each section of the book begins with teaching tips to help the adult prepare to introduce the activities to the child. In many cases there are references to easy-to-open or easy-to-use containers. Plastic zipper bags with slides, containers with lightweight plastic covers that have elastic to hold them in place, and plastic yogurt containers are good choices. If a child has difficulty opening containers, try leaving zipper bags partially unzipped or prying up one corner of the container's lid in advance of the activity.

When you begin teaching a child to use picture directions, start by having all the materials the student is going to need together and ready to use, so the focus will be on how to use a list, not how to hunt down materials. Putting exactly what the student is going to need (individual portions) in a small plastic basket or on a tray or table will help.

After the child understands how to use a list, gradually make gathering materials a little more challenging. Throw in some materials that are not needed and not on the list. Materials can be stored in easy-to-open see-through containers at first, then in opaque containers that have the picture and word label taped onto the top or side.

Once the child is able to retrieve items from containers that are within easy reach, have him start retrieving labeled containers off nearby shelves. You can also start by having one large container from which the student counts out how many he needs (one loaf of bread, each student counts out two pieces). This works on sharing and taking turns as well. Gradually progress to having students get items from where they are normally kept.

Once things are set up, direct the child to use the checklist ("You Will Need" on the activity sheet). Direct the child's attention to the picture. If the child is verbal, see if he can answer questions such as:

► What is that?

► Do we have that? Where?

► Should we check it off?

► Do we have everything on the list? Is everything checked off?

► What do we do now?

If the child is able to give an answer, then repeat and expand on what is said. For example, if the child says, "bread," you might say, "Yes, two pieces of bread; one, two." If the child cannot state the answer, then you say it.

The picture directions are designed so the written instructions, numbers and pictures can be cut apart and each element used separately. You can also leave them intact and cover the text or numbers when photocopying, or cover the pictures and copy only the text.

They can be presented to the child in a number of ways.

► The simplest and easiest method for the child to follow is to present one direction at a time (each direction cut out and mounted or glued onto a separate card). It's not always necessary to start here, and obviously you would want to move away from this approach as soon as possible. However, presenting directions this way will allow the child to focus solely on following one direction at a time, without dealing with the idea of sequencing.

▶ The next step in complexity is to take the set of cards with directions on them and put them on a ring or make them into a little book. Here the child can be in control of turning to the next direction when a step is completed, but still sees only one direction at a time.

▶ When you feel the child is ready, present the cards in sequential order. This can be done two at a time to start, then more. Use either a left-to-right or top-to-bottom presentation. Arrows can be added between pictures to help give the idea of moving from one to another.

▶ And finally, present the directions as they appear in the book, left to right then down to the next row.

▶ Demonstrating the Tasks

When demonstrating the tasks, use clear, simple language to tell what you are doing. Since independence is the goal, let the students lead as much as possible. First see if the children can figure out what needs to be done by asking open-ended questions, such as, "What do we do with the peanut butter?" or "Where do the batteries go?" If a student is able, have her tell you what is happening.

▶ Moving Toward Independence

The student is likely to need assistance performing the tasks, but "backward chaining" can be used to gradually build independence. Work with the child until he can independently complete the last step of the task. Once this is mastered, work on independence in the next-to-last step. Keep on moving backwards until the child can complete the entire task independently. Some tasks may be more suitable for "forward chaining," which is just the reverse. In forward chaining, start with step one, then move to step two, etc.

Since students tend to become dependent upon verbal prompts, fade these out as quickly as possible. Instead of telling the child what to do, try using some different strategies, such as simply waiting expectantly and giving the child plenty of time to carry out the tasks. Keep in mind how much processing time you need when you are thinking in a different language or figuring out something that is totally new or different to you. Wait and then wait a little longer.

If the child is still unable to complete the task, give as subtle a cue as you can — a look, a nod, or pointing to or tapping an object or picture. If more assistance is needed, use as subtle a physical prompt as you can; touch the child's elbow to move his hand in the right direction, move the necessary object closer to the child, move the child's hand onto an item he needs to pick up. Only go to hand-over-hand assistance if your more subtle prompts are getting you nowhere. While they may seem more intrusive, physical prompts are actually much easier to fade than verbal reminders.

No matter what type of prompt you are giving, you will want to start using more subtle prompts as soon as possible. Keep reminding yourself to be more and more subtle until no prompting is needed. It's easy to get into a routine of providing certain cues or reminders, even when they aren't needed.

▶Building Skills — Related Activities

Once a student can follow a picture direction independently, there are a number of activities that can help reinforce acquired skills and build new ones. Below are a few ideas to try.

▶ Student teaches student

Have a student who has mastered a task teach or demonstrate it to another student.

▶ Sequence the steps of a task

Photocopy and cut out the different steps of the directions and have the student put them in the right order. The picture directions can be glued on poster board then laminated as cards to be placed in the right order on a table or attached to a board with Velcro® You can also have your students glue the cut-out pictures onto a strip of paper in the correct order.

You may want to first introduce this task with the numbers written on the picture directions. These pictures can then be matched and placed next to numbers written on the strip. This introduces the idea of matching a number to an identical number. Once a student can do this, try covering up the numbers on the pictures when photocopying them and having the child sequence the unnumbered pictures. This will require the child to look at what's happening in the picture and to figure out which action needs to come first. If the child is working on writing, have him write the correct number on each picture.

▶ Matching text to pictures

The text from all the directions can be cut out from the pictures to provide separate text and pictures, which can then be matched.

The pictures without text can also be used in having the child tell you what is happening in the picture. This is a good strategy for working on oral language and helps the child focus on "reading" the picture.

► **Using the cloze technique**

With the cloze technique, text is presented on sentence strips or on a worksheet with select words missing. The child can either write in the missing word or place a card with the correct word in the blank space.

► **Matching concept and concept phrases**

Key concept phrases like "put in" or "put on" can be written on cards and matched with pictures showing that particular action. The child can then be asked to separate pictures that represent the different concepts.

Important — Teachers Read This!

Why Use Picture Directions?

Using picture directions builds independence, which is the ultimate goal for any child. By learning to follow step-by-step picture directions, a child gains the lifelong skill of following written directions without adult assistance. Even with picture directions, most children will need to have the tasks in this book demonstrated. But with picture directions, the child will be able to independently perform tasks more quickly than otherwise possible. For a child with auditory processing difficulties or for one who needs tasks to be more concrete or visual this is even more true. Learning to complete given tasks without adult assistance builds a "can do" attitude, which encourages the child to progress in learning without always waiting for adult direction.

By beginning each activity with a checklist of items you will need, the child learns the skill of using a list. First the child needs to be able to match the actual object with the picture and to determine when all needed items are present and understand that it's time to begin the activity.

Picture directions also help teach the idea of sequencing — (recognizing numbers and following them in order, following a left-to-right and top-to-bottom progression) and the importance of performing directions in a sequential order.

Using picture directions builds reading skills as well. Because picture directions are always paired with simple, repetitive text, the child can start building associations between the written word, the pictures, and the actions performed. Additional follow-up activities (presented in "How to Use Picture Directions," on the preceding pages) can be used to build greater language and reading skills.

Cooking

Teaching Tips

▶ Orange Drink

Put just slightly more orange drink mix than needed in a small, individual container that is easily opened. Yogurt containers work well. Use a small, child-sized pitcher with approximately the right amount of water. (Small pitchers are available from early childhood supply catalogs.)

Often when children are first learning to pour, they do not know when to stop pouring. To avoid spills in the beginning, limit the amount of water you put into the pitcher so the cup cannot overflow. You might gradually increase the amount so that slight spills occur if the child does not stop pouring in time.

Another way to cue the child to avoid spills is to mark a fill line with colored tape or waterproof marker on the outside of a clear plastic cup. When initially teaching this task, pick a specific verbal cue such as, "look and pour" or "stop at the line."

To help the child count out the right number of spoonfuls of orange drink mix, use a set of three cards; after adding each spoonful, turn over one card. When the last card is turned over, the child is finished adding orange drink mix.

Stirring can present problems if the child doesn't stir long enough or keeps stirring and stirring. If the child can count by rote, teach him to count to a certain number while stirring. Or teach the child to say a verse or sing a song that ends when the stirring is finished.

> I am stirring, I am stirring.
> Stir. Stir. Stir.
> I'm all done. I'm all done.
> STOP!

▶ Chocolate Milk

Use a small easy-to-open container to hold enough milk to fill the child's cup two-thirds to three-fourths full, leaving room for the chocolate powder and stirring without spilling. A small plastic container with a pop-open tab on top works well. If the tab fits too tightly for the child to pry open, leave it slightly ajar. A colored dot added to the top of the tab will help the child see where to pull. You can also use a small plastic container with a built-in plastic pop-up straw, although the liquid sometimes pours out slowly or in spurts and can be distracting to the child.

Start out by giving the child slightly more than two tablespoons of chocolate powder in a small, easy-to-open container. Once the child has learned to spoon out two spoonfuls and stop, start giving the child a larger container of chocolate powder.

If the child needs help with stirring, refer back to the suggested cues for making Orange Drink (see above).

▶Peanut Butter Face

To start, put just enough or a little more peanut butter than is needed (approximately two to three tablespoons) into a small, easy-to-open container. Cut a thin slice of red apple, leaving the peel on, and put with two raisins into another easy-to-open container. Later, progress to having the child count out two raisins from a larger container.

▶Tortilla Roll-Up

Use a small (6-inch) tortilla placed on a plate. Provide a small amount of soft butter, soft cream cheese or mayonnaise in a small, easy-to-open container. Use thin-sliced lunch meat torn or cut into small pieces.

▶Peanut Butter Sandwich

Start with individual portions of peanut butter, jelly and bread in easy-to-open containers. Screw-on tops can be introduced for children who are ready to take on this fine motor task.

It is usually necessary to limit the amount of peanut butter and jelly to reasonable amounts, as children will often keep piling on more.

Two slices of bread can be placed in a zipper bag. If the child finds these too difficult, leave the bag unzipped or partially unzipped.

▶Cereal

Use the small, individual boxes of cereal that are sold in the variety packs. Each box is approximately one ounce.

Make a small fold or tab of colored tape on the top flap of the cereal box. Slip your finger under the tab to loosen the top flap so it can be more easily pulled open by the child. Different cereal boxes have different perforations for opening, but the child will learn sooner by consistently opening the box a set way, and opening the top flap will prepare him for opening regular sized boxes of cereal.

Provide just enough milk (½ cup is plenty) in an easy-to-open container.

▶Ants on a Log

Cut celery into pieces approximately three inches long, and put a small amount of peanut butter into a small, easy-to-open container.

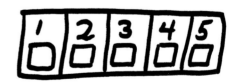

Make a number board for counting out five raisins, as shown.

▶Lunch Meat Sandwich

When first presenting this activity, you will probably want to give the child two slices of bread and one slice of lunch meat. Later you can have the child take the right amounts from a package. Use thicker sliced lunch meat for easier handling. Put two slices of bread into a plastic zipper bag. Put one slice of lunch meat into another zipper bag.

Put a small amount of butter, mayonnaise or mustard into a small, easy-to-open container.

▶Cheese and Crackers

Start by giving each child individual portions, probably one slice of cheese and four crackers. Using the individually wrapped pieces of cheese will keep it from sticking to other surfaces. A colored tab (a folded piece of plastic colored tape) can be attached to the cheese wrapper to make it easier to open.

▶Pudding

This recipe is set up for each child to have individual portions of ingredients. At some point you could try having children share a container of pudding, but the milk needs to be measured out ahead of time and put into a separate container, since measuring out liquids is much more difficult than spooning out dry ingredients.

To provide a visual reminder for counting out spoonfuls, use numbered cards as mentioned in the teaching tips for orange drink (see page 9).

Test out containers for shaking the pudding ahead of time to see if they leak. The less expensive storage containers usually work better because they are easier to open and close, especially if the lids have tabs on them. If you're going to use a new container, open and close it a number of times to loosen it up a bit.

For the final step, a digital timer works best because you can pre-set the time for five minutes, then have the child push the start button. Many digital timers come with a large red start button. If more emphasis is needed to indicate where to push, attach a brightly colored circle cut out of poster board to the start button.

▶Traffic Light Crackers

Provide each child with one section (one quarter) of a graham cracker and a flat plate or placemat to put the cracker on.

Color the candies on a photocopy of the picture directions page. You might also want to highlight or underline the color words in the correct color.

A separate task children can do ahead of time is to sort the candies into two groups, one containing the yellow, red and green candies, and another containing all the other colors. Another task children can do is to break each graham cracker into four sections.

▶Trail Mix

Keep each food item in a separate, easy-to-open container that is see-through or has a picture of the item it contains on the outside. Don't use a zipper bag, as this is what the child will be putting the items into to make the trail mix. You may want to start with just the right number of items so the child will know that he counted out correctly. When this has been mastered, move on to having the child count out the right number from a larger container.

Provide a counting board with 10 spaces on it where the child can place the food items to count them. Sometimes making a small box with a marker or a colored piece of paper under each number helps clarify the idea of placing an item there.

▶Egg Nog

The recipe for one child-sized serving of eggnog is as follows:
- ▶ 2 tablespoons egg substitute
- ▶ ½ cup milk with ¼ teaspoon vanilla
- ▶ 1 tablespoon sugar with a dash of salt and nutmeg
- ▶ 3 easy-to-open containers

Put 2 tablespoons of the egg substitute mixture into a small, easy-to-open container, and label the container with a word or picture or both.

Put ½ cup milk with ¼ teaspoon vanilla into an easy-to-open and easy-to-pour container and label it.

Put 1 tablespoon sugar with a dash of salt and nutmeg into a small, easy-to-open container and label it.

The container the child uses for mixing together the egg, milk and sugar should have a pour spout so the child can pour her eggnog into a cup. You can use a bowl with a pour spout, a large measuring cup or a small pitcher.

▶Banana Cookies

Cut a banana in half with the peel on and bend back the edge of the peel for easier peeling. Give each child half of a banana.

Put ½ cup of graham cracker crumbs into a plastic zipper bag.

Orange Drink

You will need

☐ Orange drink

☐ Water

☐ Cup

☐ Spoon

1

Open orange
drink mix.

2

Put 3 spoons
of mix in cup.

3

Pour water
in cup.

4

Stir.

Chocolate Milk

You will need

- [ ] Cup

- [ ] Chocolate mix

- [ ] Milk

- [ ] Spoon

1

Open
chocolate mix.

2

Put 2 spoons of
chocolate mix
in cup.

3

Pour milk
in cup.

4

Stir.

Peanut Butter Face

You will need

- [ ] Rice cake

- [ ] Peanut butter

- [ ] Apple slice

- [ ] 2 raisins

- [ ] Knife

1

Put peanut butter on rice cake.

2

Put apple slice on rice cake.

3

Put 1 raisin on rice cake.

4

Put 1 more raisin on rice cake.

Tortilla Roll-Up

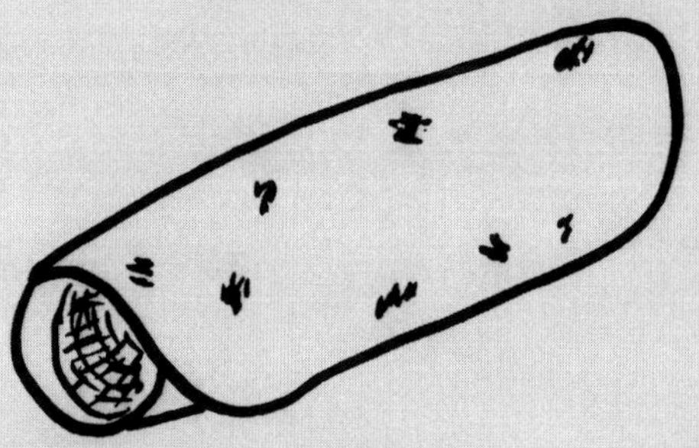

You will need

- ☐ Tortilla 
- ☐ Spread 
- ☐ Meat 
- ☐ Knife

1 Put spread on tortilla.

2 Put meat on tortilla.

3 Fold tortilla.

4 Roll up tortilla.

Peanut Butter Sandwich

You will need

☐ Peanut butter

☐ Jelly

☐ 2 slices of bread

☐ Knife

1

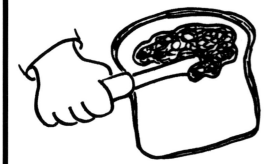

Put jelly on 1 slice of bread.

2

Put peanut butter on 1 slice of bread.

3

Put the 2 slices of bread together.

4

Cut.

Cereal

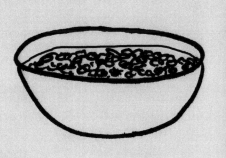

You will need

- ☐ Cereal

- ☐ Milk

- ☐ Bowl

- ☐ Spoon

1

Pull open.

2

Pull open.

3

Pull up.

4

Pull open.

5

Pour cereal in bowl.

6

Pour milk in bowl.

Ants on a Log

You will need

☐ Celery

☐ Peanut butter

☐ Raisins

☐ Knife

1

Put peanut
butter on celery.

2

Count out
5 raisins.

3

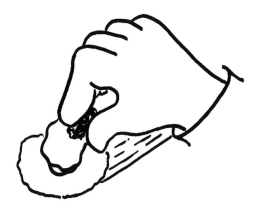

Put I raisin on
peanut butter.

4

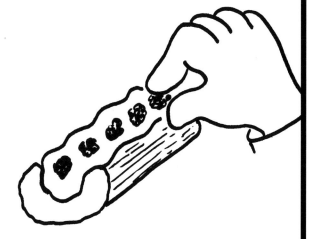

Put all the
raisins on
peanut butter.

Lunch Meat Sandwich

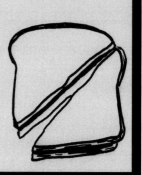

You will need

☐ Lunch meat

☐ 2 slices of bread

☐ Spread

☐ Knife

1

Put spread on 1 slice of bread.

2

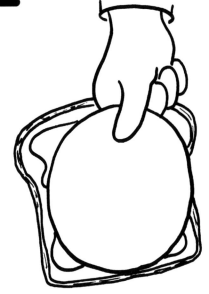

Put lunch meat on bread.

3

Put other slice of bread on top.

4

Cut.

Cheese and Crackers

You will need

☐ Cheese

☐ Crackers

☐ Knife

1

Open cheese.

2

Take out cheese.

3

Cut.

4

Take 1 piece of cheese.

5

Fold.

6

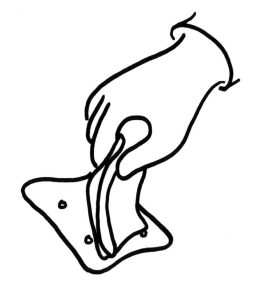

Put cheese on cracker.

7

Put a cracker on top.

Pudding

You will need

- ☐ Pudding mix
- ☐ Milk
- ☐ Container
- ☐ Bowl
- ☐ Spoon
- ☐ Timer

1

Put 2 spoons of pudding mix in container.

2

Put milk in container.

3

Put top on.

4

Shake and shake and shake.

5

Open
container.

6

Pour in bowl.

7

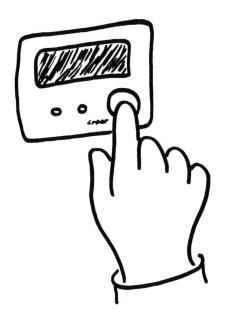

Push button on
timer and wait.

Traffic Light Cracker

You will need

☐ Graham cracker

☐ Peanut butter

☐ Candy

☐ Knife

1

Put peanut butter on cracker.

2

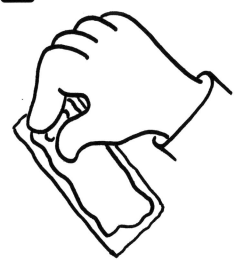

Put red candy on top.

3

Put yellow candy in the middle.

4

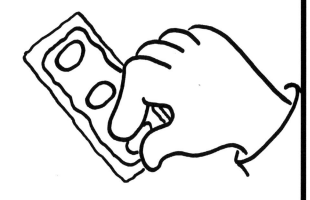

Put green candy on the bottom.

Trail Mix

You will need

☐ Raisins

☐ Cereal

☐ Mini-wheats

☐ Candy

☐ Bag

1

Count out 10 raisins.

2

Put raisins in bag.

3

Count out 10 pieces of cereal.

4

Put cereal in bag.

Count out 10 mini-wheats.

Put mini-wheats in bag.

Count out 10 candies and put in bag.

Close the bag.

Egg Nog

You will need

- ☐ Egg
- ☐ Milk
- ☐ Sugar
- ☐ Bowl
- ☐ Eggbeater
- ☐ Cup

1

Put egg in
bowl.

2

Put milk in
bowl.

3

Put sugar in
bowl.

4

Stir with
eggbeater.

5

Pour in cup.

Banana Cookies

You will need

☐ Banana

☐ Knife

☐ Graham cracker
crumbs in a zipper bag

☐ Plate

1

Pull off
banana peel.

2

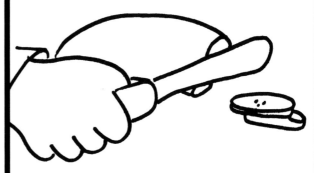

Cut banana
into pieces.

3

Open bag.

4

Put banana
pieces in bag.

5

Close bag.

6

Shake bag.

7

Open bag.

8

Take out banana
cookies and put
on plate.

Arts and Crafts

Teaching Tips

▶Greeting Card

Cut construction paper to the right size for the card. The construction paper can be pre-folded, then opened, or the fold line can be marked with a dotted line.

Use any assortment of decorations to glue on: Stickers, pictures cut out from magazines or cards, shapes cut out from construction or tissue paper, pieces of yarn or ribbon, sequins, dried flowers, tinsel, feathers, etc.

If the child is unable to write her name, the final direction to "write your name" can be dropped, or her name can be included on the pre-made message. (Creating the message, either by hand or on a computer, could be a separate activity done ahead of time with an adult.) If the child is able to trace her name, try including it on the message in highlighter for her to trace. She can also make a mark or drawing to represent her signature.

▶Shaker (Maraca)

Wipe the inside of a potato chip can and cover it with light colored construction paper.

Dried lima beans can be used to put in the shaker or, for a fine motor challenge and a more interesting sound, use a mix of smaller and larger beans.

▶Leaf Rubbing

Real leaves or leaves cut out of construction paper can be used. If using real leaves, choose ones that have a simple shape, without a lot of points and angles. Also, avoid leaves that are too dried out. Flattening them in a book ahead of time makes them easier to use.

Completely remove the wrapper from a large-sized crayon, and provide a piece of cardboard or some poster board for the child to work on.

▶Sunshine Picture

Using yellow construction paper, draw and cut out a circle approximately 3 inches in diameter. Draw a smiling face on the yellow circle.

Using yellow chalk, draw a circle with lines radiating out from it in the middle of a piece of blue construction paper.

Cut yellow paper into strips approximately one inch wide. Approximately three 8½ inch long strips will be needed for each sun picture.

▶Olympic Medal

You will need a metal lid from a frozen juice can and a piece of ribbon approximately 2½ feet long.

Attach a piece of colored plastic tape to each end of the ribbon, leaving ½ inch to 1 inch extending beyond the ribbon. Cover each sticky side of tape with a piece of wax paper.

Cut out a star shape that will fit inside the metal juice lid.

Use a small sprinkle container of glitter that does not hold much, as kids often get carried away with glitter. Old jars that once contained various spices and herbs can be filled with a small amount of glitter.

▶Fan

Cut two identical shapes, between 6 and 10 inches long and wide, out of poster board. Any basic shape can be used.

Mark on one of the cut-out shapes where the jumbo craft stick (tongue depressor) is to be placed.

Put a piece of colored plastic tape (approximately 2 inches long) on a piece of waxed paper, bending one corner of the tape up slightly so it will be easier for the child to grasp.

▶Stained Glass Window

Make a frame out of construction paper by cutting out the center part. The frame can be a simple rectangular or oval shape, or a recognizable shape such as a Christmas tree, a leaf, a boat, a snowman, etc.

Next cut a piece of clear contact paper the same size as the construction paper. Pull off the backing and attach the contact paper to the construction paper frame. Replace the backing so the frame is sandwiched between the contact paper and the backing. A corner of the backing can be folded back.

Tissue paper looks great for decorating the window, but is more difficult to cut and handle. Colored copier or construction paper can be used instead.

▶Peppermint Wreath

Cut a wreath shape from a 6-inch square of green poster board. Make a bow out of red curling ribbon and attach it to a piece of wax paper with double sided scotch tape.

Draw seven one-inch circles on the wreath to indicate where to glue the peppermint candies. Candies can be glued on with wrapper on or with wrapper removed. If you want to use unwrapped candies, remove the candy wrappers ahead of time.

Make an X on the wreath to show where the bow will go.

▶Playdough

This is a small portion, no-cook playdough that a child can make up independently.

You will need:
  1 cup flour
  ¼ cup salt
  ½ cup water

Use a one-cup and a ¼-cup measuring cup made for measuring dry ingredients.

Provide color coded labels on the measuring cups and on the flour and salt. For example, attach a blue paper label with clear contact paper or tape to the one-cup measuring cup and the container of flour, and an orange label to the ¼ cup measuring cup and the salt.

Have ½ cup of water already measured and available in an easy-to-open container or in a small pitcher or cup.

The longer the playdough is kneaded, the better. Set the timer for a length of time that is reasonable for the child to continue kneading, perhaps one to three minutes.

The playdough will keep for an extended period of time in an airtight container. Shapes can be made out of the dough and air dried for a few days until hard or baked in a 300° F oven.

▶Painted Egg

Fill in the blanks on the picture directions with the words for the colors you plan to use. Then add these colors to the pictures. You might want to highlight or underline the color words with the appropriate color as well.

Draw a large egg shape on a piece of white construction paper. The egg can be any size, but try to keep the egg small enough that the child can paint the entire surface of the egg before losing interest.

Put a small amount of condensed milk in two separate, easy-to-open containers. Add a different color of food coloring to each.

Provide the child with two small paint brushes. The brushes can be color coded to match the color of paint by putting a small piece of colored plastic tape on each brush.

When the child is finished painting, hang the egg up at an angle so the paint will run together to make interesting patterns. When dry, the evaporated milk leaves a shiny finish.

►Matching Game

Using five unlined index cards, draw a line down the middle of each card (top to bottom)with a marker.

Provide the child with five sets of stickers, making sure each set contains two identical medium-to-large stickers. Use individual stickers or cut stickers out so that each is separate. This is to help clarify that only one sticker goes on each index card.

Put each set of stickers in a separate container or compartment; use a muffin tin, egg carton, a box with sections or individual, or small disposable bathroom cups.

Pull off the part of the sticker sheet that surrounds it so all that remains is the actual sticker on the backing. Then slightly bend up one edge of the sticker or bend back a corner of the backing.

After the child has made the cards, he can play a matching game by laying them out, face down, on the table and turning them over two at a time trying to find matches.

This could be done as an individual activity at first, then as a game with another child.

►Tree Collage

If the child is unable to cut out a shape, cut out the tree shape ahead of time and drop step #1 from the directions. You can work on emerging cutting skills by cutting out part of the shape and leaving pieces for the child to cut off.

Provide each child with a cut out star and an assortment of decorations for the tree (colored balls cut out of construction paper or wrapping paper, pieces of tinsel or foil, ribbon, yarn, etc.).

▶Snow Picture 1

Glue a piece of white paper, cut to look like snow on the ground, onto a piece of blue construction paper.

With a marker, make a basic triangle-shaped tree on green paper. For children who have difficulty with cutting, cut out part of the tree, leaving sections for the child to cut off (as was suggested for Tree Collage, page 52).

Cut out a snowman, creating your own or using the pattern given.

Add a small amount of water to liquid school glue to thin it to a consistency that can be easily brushed on with a paint brush. Keep glue in an easy-to-open container.

Put a small amount of rice (2 to 3 tablespoons) in a small, easy-to-open container with a wide opening.

Snow Picture 2

Use the pattern below or your own pattern to create circles in three sizes. Provide the child with one of each sized circle, each on a separate piece of paper. The eyes, nose and buttons should already be on the circles before they are given to the child.

Cut a hat for the snowman out of black construction paper. Glue white paper onto the bottom of a piece of blue construction paper to look like snow on the ground.

Use white chalk to trace the circles onto the blue background to indicate where the child should glue the circles to make a snowman.

Add enough water to liquid school glue that the glue can be easily brushed on with a paint brush. Keep glue in an easy-to-open container.

Put a small amount of rice (2 to 3 tablespoons) in a small, easy-to-open container with a wide opening.

▶Lei Necklace

Cut circular flower shapes approximately 1½ inches in diameter out of construction paper and punch a hole in the middle using a hole punch. Each lei will use six to eight flowers and six to eight pieces of rigatoni pasta. Put flowers and rigatoni in separate containers or in separate compartments of a divided container.

Roll a 2-inch piece of tape tightly around one end of a 2-foot piece of yarn as shown.

Fold back the other end of the yarn to form a loop and tie a knot big enough so that a paper flower with a hole in it can't slip over it. Tape the loop onto a table, a piece of poster board or a cookie sheet.

Put the first flower on and slide it until it reaches the knot in the yarn.

Provide a model for children to follow by copying the pattern below. Alternating flowers and pasta can also be glued on poster board as a guide.

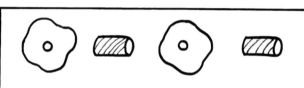

▶Holiday Ornament

Using the fronts of old greeting cards, cut around the outer edge of the card, rounding the edges. You can also cut out part of the card, such as a snowman or wreath.

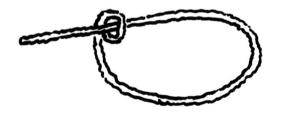

Punch one hole in the top of the card with a hole punch. Using a 12-inch pipe cleaner, make a loop on one end as shown.

Thin some liquid school glue with a small amount of water and put into a small, easy-to-open container.

Greeting Card

You will need

☐ Paper

☐ Glue

☐ Pencil

☐ Decorations

☐ Message

1 Fold paper.

2 Put glue on.

3 Put on decorations.

4 Open card.

5

Put glue on.

6

Put message on.

7

Write your name.

Shaker (Maraca)

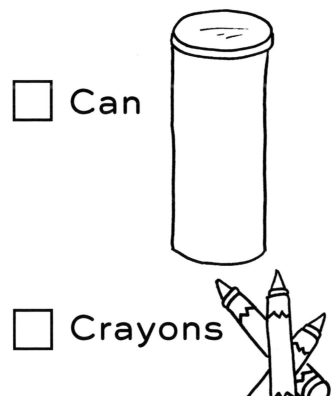

You will need

☐ Can

☐ Crayons

☐ Beans

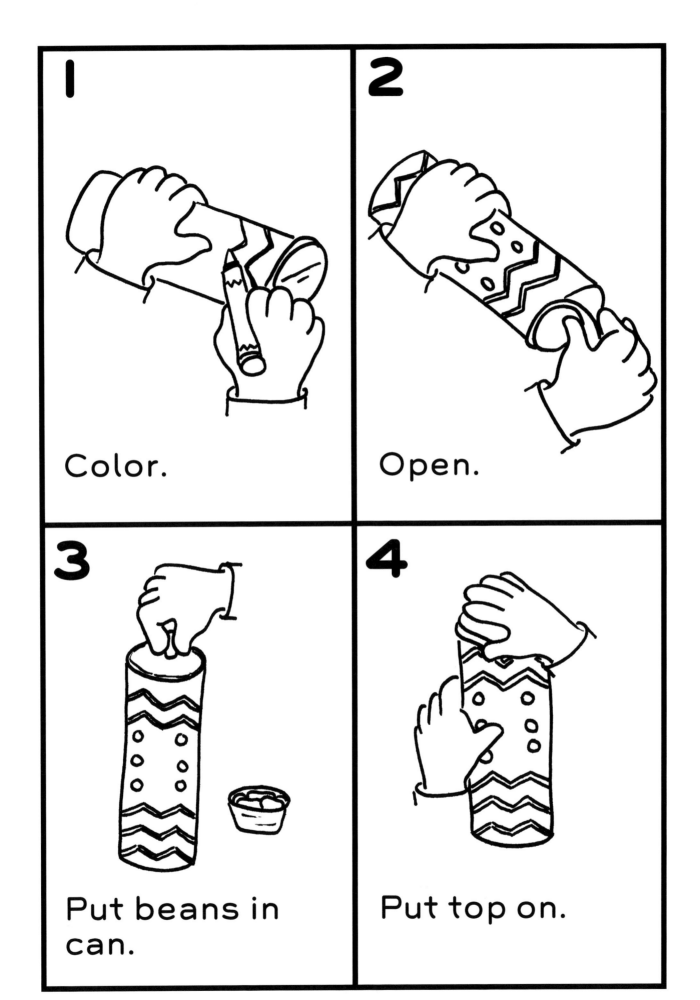

1 Color.

2 Open.

3 Put beans in can.

4 Put top on.

Leaf Rubbing

You will need

- ☐ Leaf
- ☐ Board
- ☐ Paper
- ☐ Crayon
- ☐ Glue

1

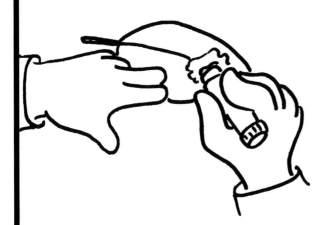

Put glue on leaf.

2

Put leaf on board.

3

Put paper on board.

4

Rub crayon all over.

Sunshine Picture

You will need

☐ Yellow face

☐ Blue paper

☐ Yellow strips of paper

☐ Glue

1

Turn yellow face over.

2

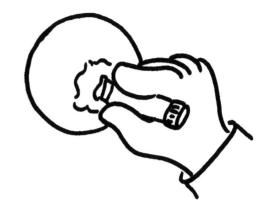

Put glue on back of yellow face.

3

Put yellow face on blue paper.

4

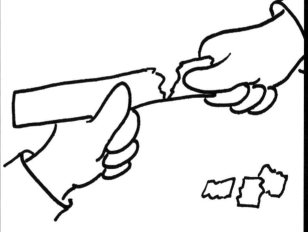

Tear yellow strips into small pieces.

5

Put glue on
yellow line.

6

Put pieces of
yellow paper
on glue.

7

Put glue and
yellow paper on
all the yellow
lines.

Olympic Medal

You will need

- ☐ Lid

- ☐ Ribbon

- ☐ Star

- ☐ Glitter *glitter*

- ☐ Glue *Glue*

1

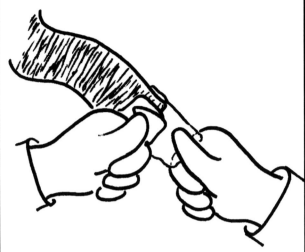

Pull paper
off tape.

2

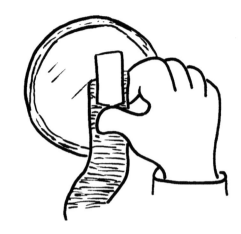

Put tape on
lid.

3

Pull paper off
tape and put
tape on lid.

4

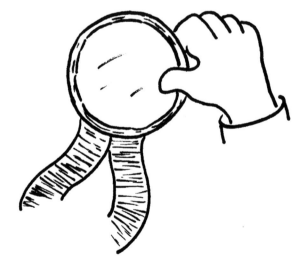

Turn lid over.

5

Put glue on
star.

6

Put star on lid.

7

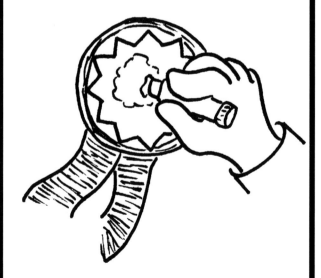

Put glue on
star.

8

Sprinkle glitter
on star.

Fan

You will need

- ☐ 2 pieces of cardboard
- ☐ Stick
- ☐ Tape
- ☐ Glue

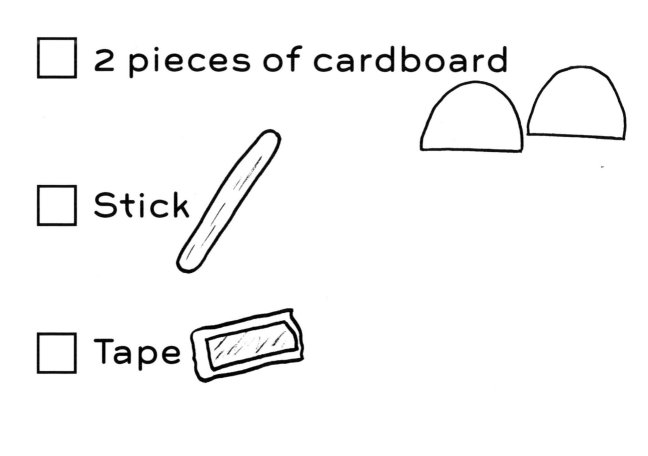

1

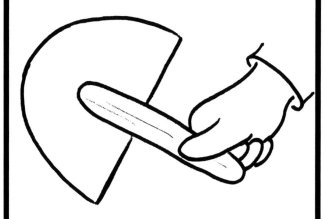

Put stick on
cardboard.

2

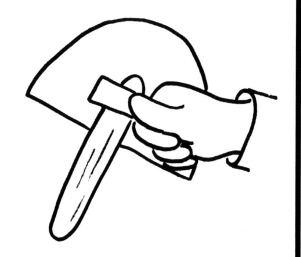

Pull tape off
and put tape
over stick.

3

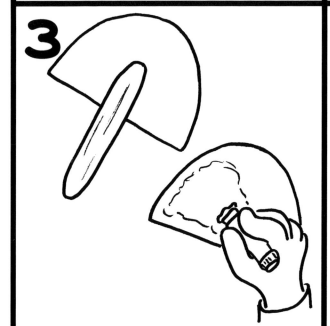

Put glue all
over cardboard.

4

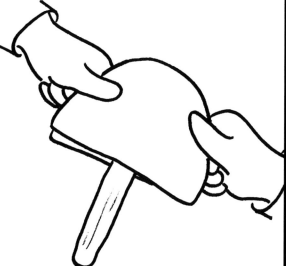

Put other
cardboard on
top.

5

Press down.

6

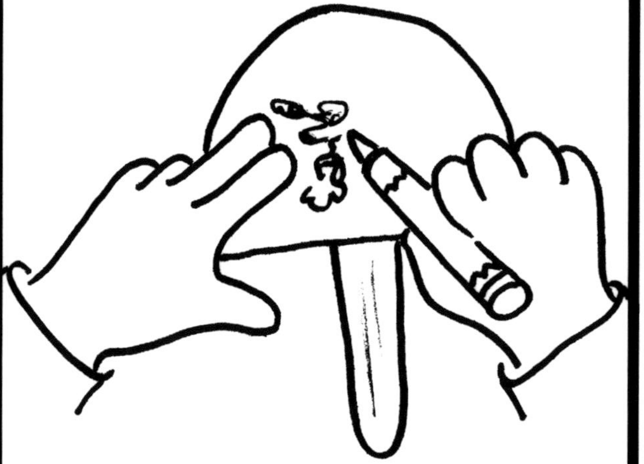

Color fan.

Stained Glass Window

You will need

☐ Picture frame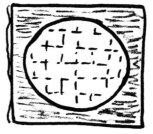

☐ Colored paper

☐ Scissors

1

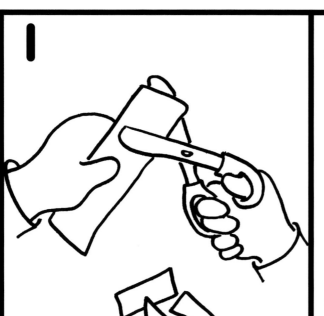

Cut colored paper.

2

Pull white paper off picture frame.

3

Put 1 piece of colored paper on the picture frame.

4

Put more pieces of colored paper on the picture frame.

Peppermint Wreath

You will need

- ☐ Candy
- ☐ Wreath
- ☐ Bow
- ☐ Glue

1

Put glue on
circle.

2

Put candy on
circle.

3

Put glue and
candy on all
the circles.

4

Pull bow off
and put bow
on X.

Playdough

You will need

- [ ] Flour

- [ ] Salt

- [ ] Water

- [ ] Bowl

- [ ] Spoon

- [ ] 2 measuring cups

- [ ] Timer

1

Fill the large cup with flour.

2

Put flour in bowl.

3

Fill small cup with salt.

4

Put salt in bowl.

5

Put water in bowl.

6

Stir.

7

Set timer.

8

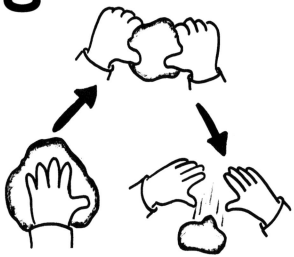

Knead dough.

Painted Egg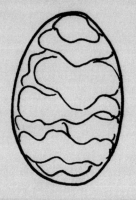

You will need

☐ Paper egg

☐ Scissors

☐ _____ paint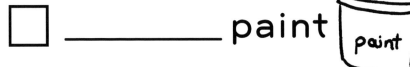

☐ _____ paint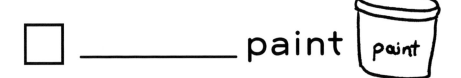

☐ 2 paint brushes

1

Cut out egg.

2

Paint part of egg with _____ paint.

3

Paint part of egg with _____ paint.

4

Paint more of egg with _____ paint.

5

Paint more
of egg with
_____ paint.

6

Keep painting
until all of the
egg is covered.

Matching Game

You will need

☐ 5 cards

☐ Stickers

☐ Scissors

☐ Bag

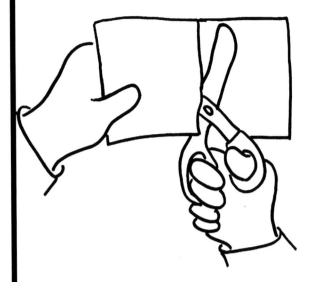

Cut all the cards on the line.

Put 1 sticker on a card.

Put each sticker on a card.

Put all the cards in a bag. Close the bag.

Tree Collage

You will need

- [ ] Paper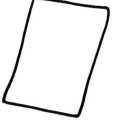

- [ ] Scissors

- [ ] Glue

- [ ] Christmas tree

- [ ] Star

- [ ] Decorations

1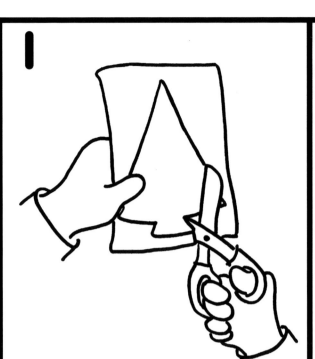

Cut out Christmas tree.

2

Put glue on tree.

3

Put Christmas tree on paper.

4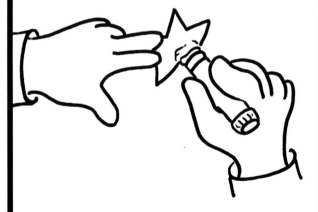

Put glue on star.

5

Put star on
top of tree.

6

Put glue on
Christmas
tree.

7

Put decorations
on Christmas
tree.

Snow Picture 1

You will need

- [ ] Blue paper
- [ ] Tree
- [ ] Snowman
- [ ] Glue stick *Glue*
- [ ] Brush
- [ ] Glue *glue*
- [ ] Rice *rice*

1 Cut out tree.

2 Put glue on tree.

3 Put tree on picture.

4 Put glue on snowman.

5

Put snowman
on picture.

6

Brush glue all
over picture.

7

Sprinkle rice all
over picture.

Snow Picture 2

You will need

- ☐ Blue paper
- ☐ 3 white circles
- ☐ Snowman hat
- ☐ Glue stick
- ☐ Brush
- ☐ Glue
- ☐ Rice

1

Cut out all
the circles.

2

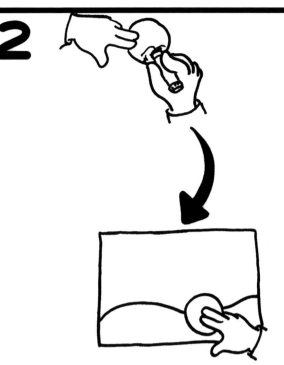

Put glue on large
circle. Put the
circle on paper.

3

Put glue on
medium circle.
Put the circle on.

4

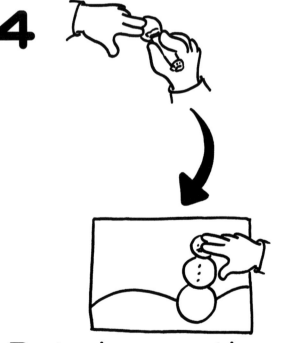

Put glue on the
small circle.
Put the circle on.

5

Put glue on hat.
Put the hat on.

6

Brush the glue
all over the
picture.

7

Sprinkle rice
all over the
picture.

Lei Necklace

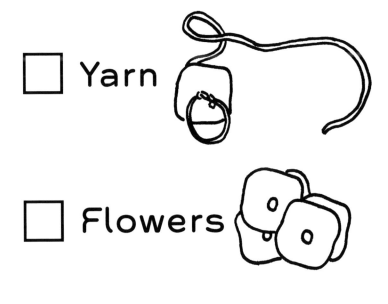

You will need

☐ Yarn

☐ Flowers

☐ Pasta

1

Pick up yarn and pick up pasta.

2

Put yarn through pasta.

3

Hold up yarn and push pasta down.

4

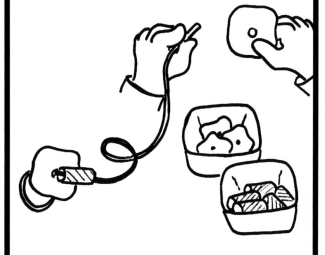

Pick up yarn and pick up flower.

5

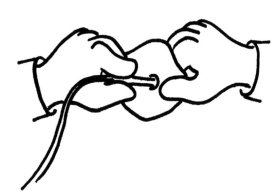

Put yarn
through flower.

6

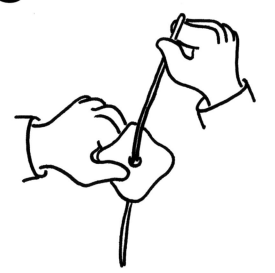

Hold up yarn
and push
flower down.

7

Put on all the
pasta and
flowers.

Holiday Ornament

You will need

- ☐ Pipe cleaner ━━━━━━━━━━

- ☐ Card

- ☐ Glue *glue*

- ☐ Brush

- ☐ Glitter *glitter*

1

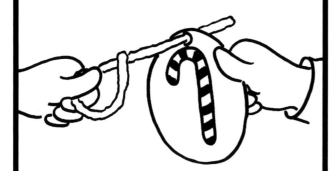

Put pipe cleaner through the hole.

2

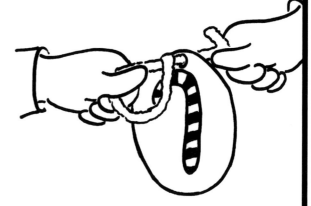

Bend pipe cleaner.

3

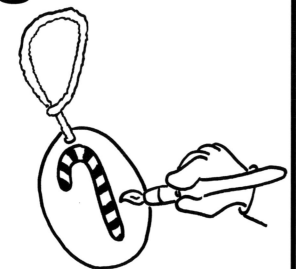

Brush card with glue.

4

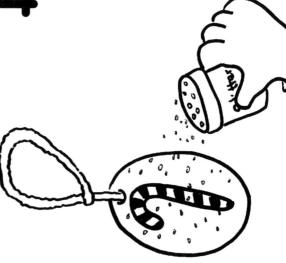

Shake on glitter.

Life Skills

Teaching Tips

►Folding Washcloths

Folding laundry is often a difficult task to teach because students can't see exactly where to fold or how. By adding dots to match, the task becomes more clearly defined and, therefore, easier to learn. The directions use washcloths because they are small and easy to handle. Once the student has figured out washcloths, the same technique can be used to fold small towels and, finally, full-sized bath towels.

Use waterproof markers or small pieces of iron-on or sew-on fabric to add dots to the washcloths. Be sure to place the dots so that when the washcloth is correctly folded the same-colored dots touch each other. On one side, place four blue dots as shown.

On the other side place four red dots as shown.

If the student has difficulty placing the washcloth in the right position to start, then place a piece of colored tape on the table surface and have him first line up the washcloth with the tape. If further clarity is needed, place colored tape in a square and have the student place the washcloth inside the square.

►Giving a Present

The key to success with this activity is finding a sturdy gift box that is easily opened and closed. Use a new bow that still has the backing on the sticky part or apply an easily removed backing to a recycled bow. Attaching a tab (a small piece of plastic or folded colored plastic tape) between the backing and the sticky part can make removing the backing easier.

►Photo Album

Use a trading card refill page with nine slots for pictures per page. You will probably want to start with fewer than nine slots, in which case you can carefully cut between the rows or between the columns. That way you can start out with three, four or six, depending on how you cut the page.

Put the refill page inside a loose leaf binder.

Attach a small piece of colored plastic tape at the top of each picture slot by folding it over the top.

Provide the correct number of trading cards or laminated photos to fit into the slots of the page.

►Goody Bag

Put pretzels in a dish, bowl or an easy-to-open container. It's best not to use a zipper bag as you will be using one for the finished goody bag.

Make a board for counting out the pretzels. You can use a simple board with spaces numbered 1 through 5, or, if more cueing is needed, provide a counting board with pictures of pretzels on it. The pretzel picture at right can be used for this.

Start the child with one baggy with five pretzels, then move on to having her fill two baggies (five pretzels each), etc.

It's best to establish a system that can be used when the child is filling a number of bags. Start with the container of pretzels to the child's left, then the counting board and zipper bags, then a "finished" box where the bags of pretzels will go.

►Sending a Letter

This activity can be used to send a letter or picture to a parent or friend or as a pretend or practice activity using scrap paper. To keep the directions brief, no writing or preparation of a letter has been included. An instructor may wish to work with the child in completing a letter or picture ahead of time, or you can use any printed material or picture.

If actually mailing the letter, write the name and address on the envelope in advance, or have it printed on a label for the child to attach to the envelope. You can also write the address on paper for the child to cut out and glue onto the envelope.

Choose a size of paper that will fit into the envelope when folded only one time. Fold the paper ahead of time, then unfold it and straighten it out. Add colored dots to the top and bottom of the page to be matched.

Use non-toxic marker to outline the edge of the envelope's adhesive where the child will lick.

On the front of the envelope, mark where the stamp will be placed.

Cut a stamp (if actually mailing letter) or a sticker from a roll or sheet. If needed, bend an edge of the stamp up or bend an edge of the backing down.

▶Egg Surprises

When first introducing this activity, use only two or three colored plastic eggs, taken apart, with the bottoms in a box or tray placed to the left of the child and the tops in another container placed to the right.

Find a box that is approximately 6½ inches long, 3½ inches wide, and 1½ inches deep. (The boxes that new checks often come in work well.) Use both the bottom and the top of the box to give it more strength. If the box has a distracting design on it, you can cover it with colored paper.

Cut a hole approximately 1½ inches in diameter in the top of the box. The hole should be just large enough for the bottom of an egg to sit in, but not so large that the egg will slip through when pushed on.

Put numbers on the box to help with counting out candies.

Put the correct number of candies (e.g., six candies for three eggs) into a small box or tray.

Place a small basket to the child's right where the filled eggs can go.

▶Flashlight

Since putting batteries in a flashlight does require unscrewing and screwing on the top, the child needs to have the basic concept and fine motor coordination to do it. Some pre-teaching and practice ahead of time with easy-to-open jars will probably be necessary for many children. Select a flashlight with an easy-to-use on-and-off switch.

The main cause of confusion is deciding which way the batteries go in. This can be clarified by cutting a small arrow out of colored tape and attaching it to the side of the battery to indicate which end goes down into the flashlight.

Folding Washcloths

You will need

- ☐ Washcloths

1

Put washcloth on table. See the blue dots.

2

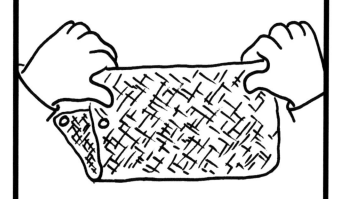

Fold. Put blue dots on top of blue dots.

3

Fold. Put red dots on top of red dots.

4

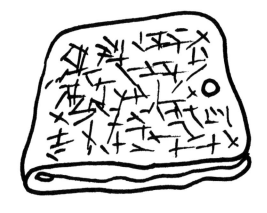

Folded washcloth.

Giving a Present

You will need

☐ Present

☐ Box

☐ Bow

1

Put present
in box.

2

Put top on box.

3

Pull paper off
bow.

4

Put bow on
box.

Photo Album

You will need

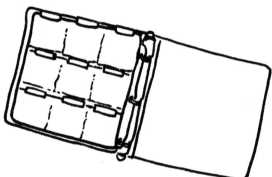

☐ Photo album

☐ Pictures

1

Pull open.

2

Put picture in.

3

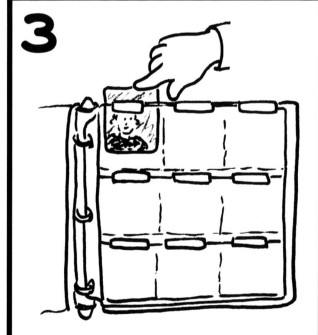

Push down.

4

Put all the
pictures in.

Goody Bag

You will need

☐ Pretzels

☐ Bag

☐ Counting board

1

Put pretzels on board.

2

5 pretzels.

3

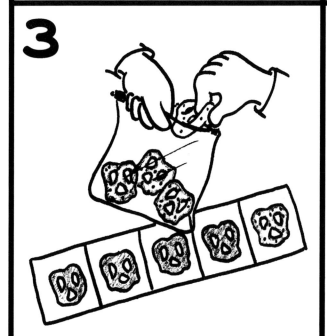

Put 5 pretzels in bag.

4

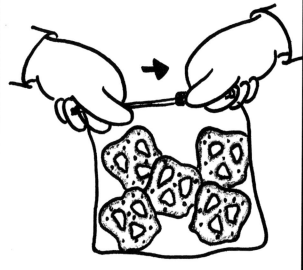

Close bag.

Sending a Letter

You will need

☐ Letter

☐ Envelope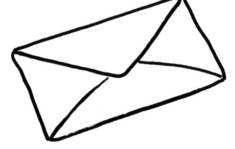

☐ Stamp

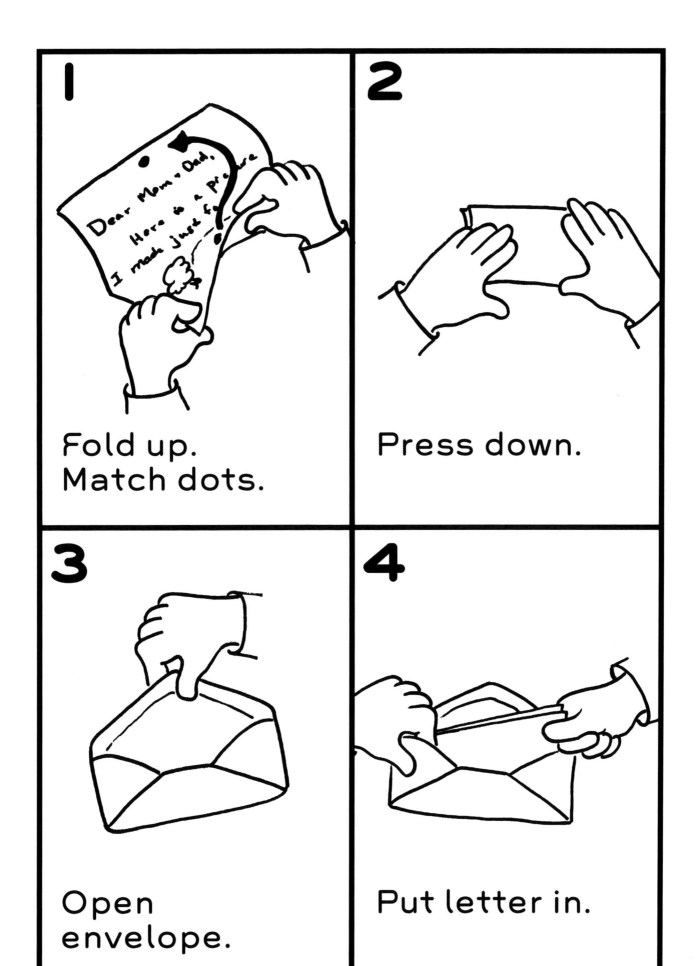

1 Fold up.
Match dots.

2 Press down.

3 Open
envelope.

4 Put letter in.

5

Lick.

6

Press down.

7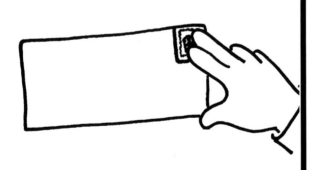

Put stamp on.

Egg Surprises

You will need

☐ Egg bottoms

☐ Egg tops

☐ Candy

☐ Box

☐ Basket

1

Put bottom of egg in hole.

2

Put 2 candies on.

3

Put 2 candies in.

4

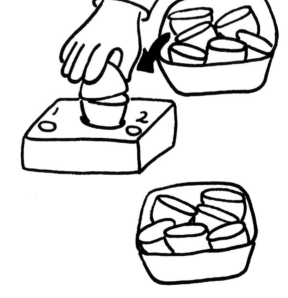

Put top on.

5

Push down.

6

Put egg in basket.

7

Put candy in all the eggs.

Flashlight

You will need

☐ Flashlight

☐ 2 batteries

1 Open.

2 Put 1 battery in.

3 Put other battery in.

4 Put top on.

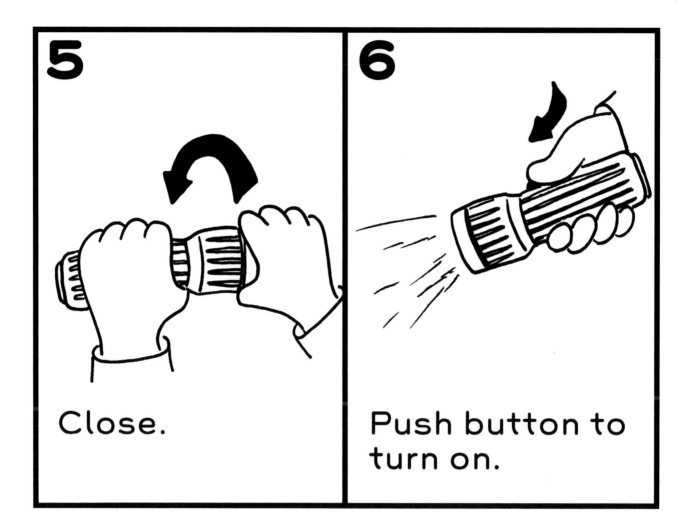

5 Close.

6 Push button to turn on.

Play Skills

Teaching Tips

▶ Playdough Snakes

Put approximately ¼ cup of any type of playdough (commercial, cooked playdough or the uncooked playdough recipe included in this book on page 51) into a small plastic zipper bag.

Create a mat for rolling out the snakes by drawing places for them on a piece of construction paper and laminating it.

▶ Potato Head

The standard Mr. Potato Head® set is used in this activity. Put out only those pieces you will need. They can be kept in order by poking them into a long Styrofoam meat tray that has been turned upside down or into a piece of foam board used for flower arranging.

Have the Potato Head sitting with his shoes on and the arms already attached.

Use a crayon to make a circle around each hole to match the color of the body part that will go there. The selected pieces from the standard Mr. Potato Head set use the following colors:

    lips = red
    nose = orange
    eyes = white
    ears = pink
    hat = black

In the picture directions the pieces are put in bottom to top, just the opposite of how we usually teach tasks. This is done because it is much more difficult to see and access the lower holes when items are already in the upper holes.

▶Lego® Car

Use the larger size of Legos, recommended for ages 1½ to 5 years, with the standard block measuring 2½ inches by 1¼ inches. The pieces used in this activity come in the standard box of large Legos.

Put the curved Lego on top of the car Lego. Use a permanent marker to draw a thick line on the curved block and on the car Lego as shown. Do the same on the other side. Take the Legos apart before giving them to the child.

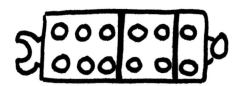

Draw two lines on the top of the car Lego as shown.

Use a permanent marker to write a "1" on both sides of the curved Lego block and a "2" on both sides of the square Lego.

▶Tinkertoy® Spinner

Attach one of the flat circular Tinkertoy discs to a piece of cardboard using double-sided tape. This is to provide a more solid base for the structure.

Put a green plastic flag in each of four yellow sticks.

Put a rounded circular disk onto one end of a red stick. On the rounded disk, indicate which holes to push the yellow sticks into by using yellow crayon.

Color the markings and Tinkertoy pieces in a photocopy of the picture directions.

If needed to clarify which piece to put in next, poke the Tinkertoy sticks through an inverted Styrofoam meat tray or into a piece of foam used for flower arrangements. The flat circular disk can be held in place by sticking a brad partially into the foam and slipping the disc onto the brad. Put the pieces in the order (left to right) they will be used.

▶ Dress a Doll

In choosing a doll, look for one with easy-to-move arms and legs. Dolls with more rounded hands work better than dolls with extended fingers that can catch on the fabric of sleeves.

Use a simple dress with one back seam. If the opening only goes down part way, use a seam ripper to open up the rest of the seam. Use one Velcro® fastener in the back at the top for closing the dress.

Use a color of Velcro that will stand out against the color of the dress, so it can be easily seen.

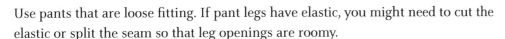

Use a dress that has large armholes. If sleeves are tight or have narrow openings, use a seam ripper to rip out part of the sleeve seam to make openings larger.

Use pants that are loose fitting. If pant legs have elastic, you might need to cut the elastic or split the seam so that leg openings are roomy.

If you don't have an appropriate dress for the doll, a simple dress can be made using the pattern provided here. If the pattern is copied at 200 percent, the dress will fit a typical small baby doll. Simply cut the pattern out of cloth, fold it in half and stitch as shown.

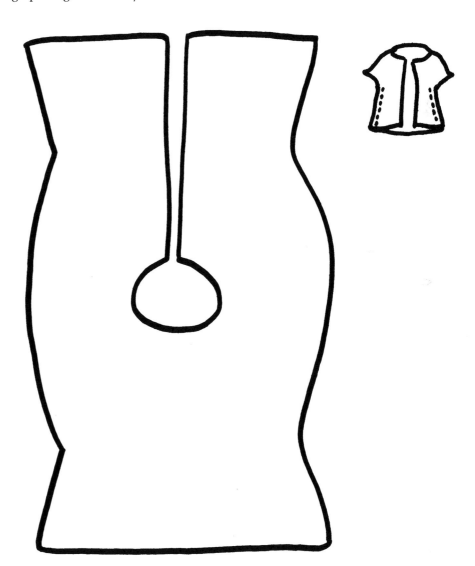

Playdough Snakes

You will need

☐ Playdough

☐ Mat

1

Take out playdough.

2

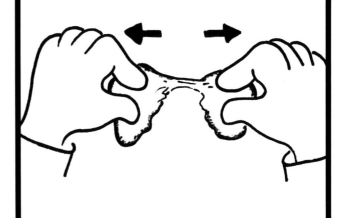

Pull into 2 pieces.

3

Put down one ball of playdough.

4

Roll ball of playdough.

5

Put snake on mat.

6

Roll other ball of playdough.

7

Put snake on mat.

Potato Head

You will need

- [ ] Potato Head

- [ ] Lips

- [ ] Nose

- [ ] Eyes

- [ ] 2 ears

- [ ] Hat

1

Put lips in red hole. | **2**

Put nose in orange hole. |
| **3**

Put eyes in white hole. | **4**

Put 1 ear in pink hole. |

5

Put other ear in pink hole.

6

Put hat on top of head.

You will need

☐ Block

☐ Block

☐ Car

☐ Man

1

Put block 1 on car.

2

Put man on car.

3

Put block 2 on car.

4

Push car and make it go.

Tinkertoy® Spinner

You will need

☐ Building board

☐ Circle

☐ Red piece

☐ 4 yellow pieces

1

Put circle on top.

2

Put red piece in.

3

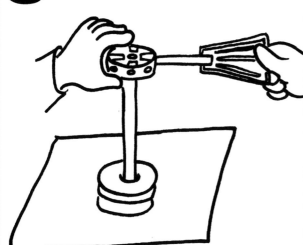

Put yellow piece in.

4

Put all of the yellow pieces in.

5

Spin.

Dress a Doll

You will need

☐ Doll

☐ Doll pants

☐ Doll dress

1

Put doll on her back.

2

Put pants on.

3

Pull pants up.

4

Put dress on top.

5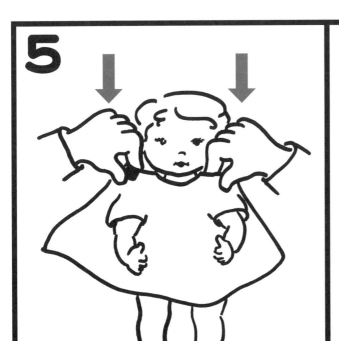

Push dress down.

6

Pick up doll.

7

Put together.

Discovery

Teaching Tips

►Dish Garden

Provide the child with a small shallow bowl, a regular table knife with a serrated edge and a carrot.

The child will also need a small, easy-to-pour container (such as a measuring cup or small teapot from a play tea set) with enough water to cover the bottom of the bowl, but not enough to flood the carrot.

Use a non-toxic marker to make a line on the carrot to indicate where to cut. A daily check off chart, as described in the "Plant a Seed" activity on page 148, can be used to keep track of watering.

►Magnetic Treasure Hunt

In this activity the child uses a magnet to find metallic objects that are hidden in a box or tray of sand. Ideas for metallic objects to use are:

   juice lid
   key ring
   paper clips
   barrette
   brads
   picture hanger
   mounting bracket for hanging picture
   nuts
   washers
   bottle opener
   miniature lock
   some keys

Put enough sand in a non-metallic pan or box to cover the bottom. Plastic storage containers with lids work well and are easy to store. Select five to 10 metallic objects to hide in the sand.

Make a counting board so the child will know how many objects he needs to find and when he is finished. This could be as simple as a counting board with spaces numbered 1 through 10 (if you have hidden 10 objects).

If the child needs more visual cues, glue or tape objects identical to the hidden objects on a board for the child to use for matching. Use photos or line drawings of the objects for children who are able to understand these.

►Bird Feeder

Poke two holes near the open end of an empty frozen juice container and tie the ends of a piece of string through each hole to make a hanger.

Stuff a wad (½ cup to ¾ cup) of playdough down inside the empty juice container. Poke a paper towel tube into the playdough to form a firm handle. Then stuff the string hanger into the can to keep it out of the way while the child makes the bird feeder.

Provide about ½ cup of birdseed in a plastic zipper bag and ⅓ to ½ cup peanut butter in an easy-to-open container.

After the child finishes making the bird feeder, pull out the cardboard tube. Usually all or most of the playdough comes out with the tube, but if some playdough remains, you can just leave it inside the can.

You may also want to tape a craft stick on the bottom of the birdfeeder to provide a perch for the birds.

►Plant a Seed

Put slightly more than the necessary amount of soil in a plastic zipper bag. You may need to leave part of the zipper unsealed to allow easier access. Use a small watering container, such as a teapot from a play tea set. Use large, fast growing seeds, such as beans or sunflower seeds.

Watering the plant could be a daily job, posted on a job board, or you could use a daily check off chart for the child to check every day after she waters her plant.

Dish Garden

You will need

☐ Carrot

☐ Knife

☐ Bowl

☐ Water

1

Cut carrot.

2

Put carrot top in bowl.

3

Put water in bowl.

4

Water every day.

Magnetic Treasure Hunt

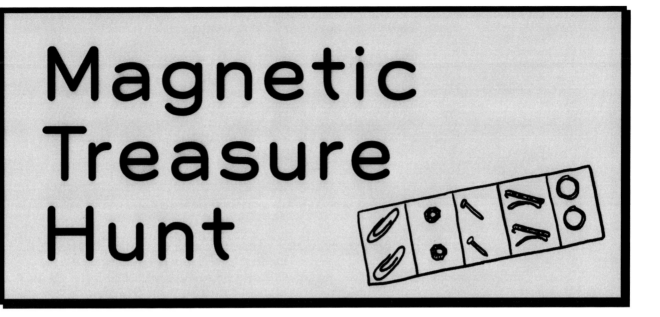

You will need

☐ Magnet

☐ Box of sand

☐ Board

1

Put magnet in sand and move it around.

2

Take off and put on board.

3

Put magnet in sand and move it around.

4

Keep looking until the board is full.

Bird Feeder

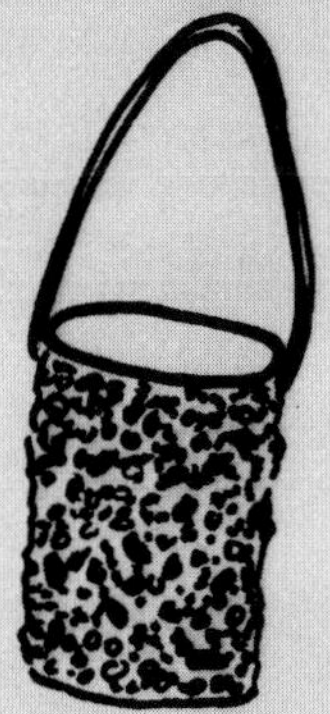

You will need

☐ Can

☐ Peanut butter

☐ Birdseed

☐ Knife

☐ Cookie sheet

1

Put peanut butter all over can.

2

Put birdseed on cookie sheet.

3

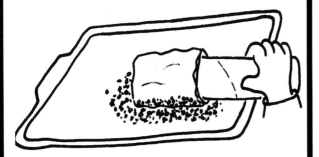

Roll can in birdseed.

4

Keep rolling until covered with birdseed.

5

Watch the birds eat lunch.

Plant a Seed

You will need

- [ ] Pot
- [ ] Soil
- [ ] Seeds
- [ ] Water
- [ ] Spoon

1

Put soil in pot.

2

Put seeds in pot.

3

Put seeds in soil.

4

Water every day.

Appendix

▶Activities by Skill Level

As children often develop different skills at different rates, the activities are rated here in two areas, fine motor and cognitive. The fine motor section ranks each activity as beginning, intermediate or more advanced, depending on what skills are required in areas such as cutting, spreading, stringing or handling small objects, etc. The cognitive section provides the same rating system (beginning, intermediate, and more advanced), but is based on how abstract and complex the concepts are that are used in the directions and how much attention is required to complete the task.

By knowing the child's areas of strengths, activities can be selected which utilize the child's strengths to build more independence. Activities can also be selected specifically to work on areas of difficulty for the child, giving more assistance as needed. It will take longer for the child to become independent in these areas, but practicing the skills in real life functional activities will reinforce his skill acquisition and build toward independence in the long run.

Fine Motor Skills

Beginning	Intermediate	More Advanced
Orange Drink	Peanut Butter Face	Tortilla Roll-Up
Chocolate Milk	Ants on a Log	Peanut Butter Sandwich
Pudding	Cheese and Crackers	Cereal
Shaker	Traffic Light Crackers	Lunch Meat Sandwich
Leaf Rubbing	Trail Mix	Egg Nog
Sunshine Picture	Banana Cookies	Painted Egg
Peppermint Wreath	Greeting Card	Snow Picture 2
Playdough	Olympic Medal	Lei Necklace
Folding Washcloths	Fan	Sending a Letter
Giving a Present	Stained Glass Window	Egg Surprises
Playdough Snakes	Matching Game	Flashlight
Treasure Hunt	Tree Collage	Tinkertoy® Spinner
Plant a Seed	Snow Picture 1	Dressing a Doll
	Holiday Ornament	Dish Garden
	Photo Album	
	Goody Bag	
	Potato head	
	Lego® Car	
	Bird Feeder	

Cognitive Ratings

Beginning	Intermediate	More Advanced
Peanut Butter Face	Tortilla Roll-Up	Orange Drink
Cereal	Peanut Butter Sandwich	Chocolate Milk
Egg Nog	Ants on a Log	Pudding
Banana Cookies	Lunch Meat Sandwich	Traffic Light Crackers
Greeting Card	Cheese and Crackers	Trail Mix
Shaker	Sunshine Picture	Peppermint Wreath
Leaf Rubbing	Olympic Medal	Playdough
Stained Glass Window	Fan	Snow Picture 2
Matching Game	Painted Eggs	Lei
Holiday Ornament	Tree Collage	Sending a Letter
Giving a Present	Snow Picture 1	Egg Surprises
Photo Album	Folding Washcloths	Tinkertoy® Spinner
Flashlight	Goody Bag	
Playdough Snakes	Potato Head	
Dish Garden	Lego® Car	
Plant a Seed	Dressing a Doll	
	Treasure Hunt	
	Bird Feeder	